CW00550765

PR

**From** *"Introduction to Soil Science:"*

Michael Barton, educated in environmental sciences, puts his knowledge to astute use in this fine primer on things ... soilish. Even though my first job was in my uncle's greenhouses way back in high school and I proved to have a green thumb throughout the years, I learned much and hope to once again get down and dirty by planting my garden. It was edifying to have read how crucial soil is to this precarious planet of ours. Dig in!!! Five easy stars!!!

— ERIC MADEEN

This book is about a comprehensive introduction to Soil Science - you'll learn everything from the basics of soil formation and classification, to the physical, chemical, and biological properties of soil, fertility and nutrient management techniques, and of course, conservation methods. In other words, this book is your one-stop shop for all your soil-related needs. You'll learn how to properly care for your soil, how to identify its many components, and how to make sure it's in the best condition possible.

— BOGDAN IVANOV

# INTRODUCTION TO SOIL SCIENCE

# INTRODUCTION TO SOIL SCIENCE

FROM FORMATION AND CLASSIFICATION TO
PHYSICAL, CHEMICAL, AND BIOLOGICAL
PROPERTIES, FERTILITY AND NUTRIENT
MANAGEMENT, AND EROSION AND
CONSERVATION

SUSTAINABLE AGRICULTURE

MICHAEL BARTON

Book
Bound Studios

*To my family, who have always supported my passion for learning and curiosity about the world around me—your love and encouragement have been the driving force behind my work. I am grateful for everything you have done to help me reach this point. Thank you for always being there for me.*

"The soil is the great connector of lives, the source and destination of all. It is the healer and restorer and resurrector, by which disease passes into health, age into youth, death into life. Without proper care for it we can have no community, because without proper care for it we can have no life."

— WENDELL BERRY

# CONTENTS

# $~~10.99~~ FREE EBOOK

**Receive Your Free Copy of Self-Sufficient Homesteading**

Or visit:
bookboundstudios.wixsite.com/michael-barton

# INTRODUCTION

Soil science studies soil as a natural resource on the Earth's surface. It is a multi-disciplinary field that encompasses the physical, chemical, biological, and ecological properties and processes in soil and is essential for understanding and managing this vital resource. **Soil is a complex and dynamic medium that supports the growth of plants.** It is crucial for maintaining the health of ecosystems. It is also an important resource for agriculture, forestry, and other land-use activities. This chapter will introduce soil science, including its definition, importance, history, and development field.

## Definition of Soil Science

Soil science is a diverse and interdisciplinary field encompassing various topics and applications. It is a required field of study, as the soil is a vital resource for the growth of plants and other land use activities and is a critical component of ecosystems worldwide. Soil scientists work to understand the properties and processes of soil and how they interact to develop strategies for managing and sustainably conserving soil resources.

Soil science involves the study of the physical, chemical, and biological properties of soil, as well as the ecological processes that occur within the soil. Physical properties of soil include things like texture, structure, and density, which can all impact soil's ability to support plants' growth. The chemical properties of soil include pH, nutrients, and organic matter, which can also influence plant growth and soil fertility. The biological properties of soil refer to the microorganisms and other organisms that live within the soil and their role in soil health and fertility. Finally, ecological processes within soil involve the interactions between soil's physical, chemical, and biological properties and how they impact the overall functioning of soil ecosystems.

Soil science also involves studying how soil forms and changes over time. Soil is created through soil formation, which involves interacting with various physical, chemical, and biological factors. These factors include climate, topography, parent material, and vegetation, which can all influence the characteristics and properties of soil. Soil scientists work to understand these factors and how they interact with one another to understand better the process of soil formation and the factors that influence soil properties.

Soil science has many applications, including agriculture, forestry and landscaping, environmental restoration, and urban and industrial settings. For example, in agriculture, soil scientists work to understand the factors that influence soil productivity and fertility and develop strategies for managing soil to maximize crop yields and promote soil health. In forestry and landscaping, soil scientists study the characteristics and needs of different soil types and develop techniques for managing soil in these settings to promote the growth of trees and other plants. In environmental restoration, soil scientists work to rehabilitate degraded soils and restore ecosystem function. And in urban and industrial settings, soil scientists work to understand the unique challenges and characteristics of soil in these environments and develop techniques for managing soil to promote the growth of plants and other land-use activities while conserving soil resources.

Overall, soil science is a vital field of study for understanding and sustainably managing soil resources. By studying the physical, chemical, and biological properties of soil, and the ecological processes that occur within the soil, soil scientists can develop strategies for managing and conserving soil resources and make important contributions to a wide range of fields.

**Importance of Soil Science**

Soil is a vital resource that is essential for supporting life on Earth. It is a complex and dynamic system comprising various physical, chemical, and biological components. **It plays a critical role in supporting the growth of plants and other land-use activities.** Soil is also a vital component of *ecosystems*. It provides a habitat for a diverse array of microorganisms and other organisms. In addition, it plays a role in the cycling of nutrients and water.

The importance of soil science cannot be overstated, as it is essential for understanding and sustainably managing soil resources. Soil science is a field of study that examines soil's physical, chemical, biological, and ecological properties and processes and how they interact with one another. In addition, soil scientists work to understand how soil forms and changes over time and can be managed and conserved to promote its long-term health and productivity.

Soil science is important for various applications, including agriculture, forestry, and other land use activities. In agriculture, soil science is essential for understanding the factors that influence soil productivity and fertility and for developing strategies for managing soil to maximize crop yields and promote soil health. In forestry, soil science is important for understanding the characteristics and needs of different types of soil and for developing techniques for managing soil to promote the growth of trees and other plants. Soil science is also important for other land use activities, such as landscaping, environmental restoration, and urban and industrial settings. It provides the knowledge and tools to understand and manage soil resources in these contexts.

Soil science is also important for understanding soil's role in maintaining ecosystems' health. Soil is a vital component of ecosystems and plays a role in cycling nutrients, water, and other resources. By studying the ecological processes that occur within the soil, soil scientists can understand how soil impacts the overall functioning of ecosystems and how it can be managed to promote ecosystem health and stability.

In summary, soil science is a critical field of study essential for understanding and sustainably managing soil resources. By studying the physical, chemical, and biological properties of soil, and the ecological processes that occur within the soil, soil scientists can develop strategies for managing and conserving soil resources and make important contributions to a wide range of fields.

**History and Development of Soil Science**

We can trace the history of soil science back to ancient civilizations, which recognized soil's importance for agriculture and other land use activities. The ancient Egyptians, for example, used irrigation and other techniques to improve soil fertility and support the growth of crops. Similarly, the ancient Greeks and Romans also recognized the importance of soil for agriculture and developed techniques for improving soil fertility and productivity.

It was in the *19th,* and *20th centuries*, however, that soil science emerged as a distinct field of study. During this time, advances in chemistry, biology, and other fields helped us better understand soil's complex properties and processes. These advances included the development of new analytical techniques for studying soil, as well as the discovery of new elements and compounds that are important for soil health and fertility.

The development of soil science also coincided with a growing recognition of the importance of soil conservation. As the human population grew and land use activities increased, there was a growing concern about the impact of these activities on soil resources. This led to the developing of new techniques and strategies for managing and conserving soil resources, such as soil conservation practices and sustainable land use practices.

Today, soil science continues to evolve and expand, with new research and innovations helping to further our understanding of this vital resource. For example, soil scientists can now use a wide range of **analytical techniques** to study soil and have made important advances in soil fertility and nutrient management, soil erosion and conservation, and soil management in different land use contexts. In addition, soil science continues to be an important field of study in the face of global challenges such as climate change and environmental degradation, as soil plays a key role in maintaining the health and stability of ecosystems.

In summary, soil science is an important field that plays a crucial role in understanding and managing soil resources. By studying the physical, chemical, biological, and ecological properties and processes of soil, soil scientists can develop techniques for conserving and improving soil quality and advise on the sustainable use of this vital resource. Furthermore, the field of soil science is constantly evolving, with new research and innovations emerging all the time. As such, it is important to continue investing in soil science research and education to ensure our soil resources' long-term health and productivity.

# SOIL FORMATION AND CLASSIFICATION

S oil formation is the process by which soil is created and develops over time. It is a complex process influenced by various factors, including climate, vegetation, geology, and the actions of living organisms. Soil classification is the process of organizing and categorizing soils based on their physical and chemical properties. This is important for understanding different soils' characteristics and potential uses and developing appropriate management practices. In this chapter, we will explore the processes of soil formation, the factors that influence it, and the classification of soils based on their physical and chemical properties.

## Processes of Soil Formation

Soil formation, also known as pedogenesis, is the process by which soil is created and develops over time. It is a complex process that involves the interaction of various physical, chemical, and biological factors. These factors interact with one another to create soil, and the specific combination of these factors influences soil characteristics in a particular location.

Physical factors influencing soil formation include climate, topography, and the actions of water, wind, and other weathering agents. Climate, for example, can influence the type of soil that forms in a particular location, as different types of soil are better suited to different climatic conditions. Topography, or the shape and slope of the land, can also influence soil formation, as different types of soil are better suited to different topographic conditions. Water, wind, and other weathering agents also play a role in soil formation, as they help to break down and erode the materials that makeup soil.

Chemical factors that influence soil formation include the presence of minerals and organic matter and the effects of acidity and pH. Different minerals can contribute to soil characteristics, such as its texture, structure, and nutrient content. Organic matter, made up of decomposed plant and animal material, is also an important component of soil, as it helps improve soil structure and fertility. Acidic or basic conditions, which are determined by the pH of the soil, can also influence soil formation, as certain types of soil are better suited to different pH conditions.

Biological factors influencing soil formation include the actions of living organisms, such as plants, animals, and microorganisms. Plants play a critical role in soil formation, as they help to break down and decompose organic matter and contribute to the nutrient content of the soil. Animals and microorganisms also play a role in soil formation, as they help to break down and decompose organic matter and contribute to the nutrient-cycling process within the soil.

Overall, soil formation is a complex process involving various physical, chemical, and biological factors. The specific combination of these factors in a particular location determines the characteristics and properties of the soil that forms in that location.

## Factors that Influence Soil Formation

Many factors can influence soil formation, including climate, vegetation, geology, and the actions of living organisms. Understanding these factors is important for understanding how soil forms and changes over time and developing strategies for managing and conserving soil resources.

Climate is one of the most important factors influencing soil formation, as it determines the amount of rainfall, temperature, and other weather patterns in an area. Different soil types are better suited to different climatic conditions, and the specific combination of climatic conditions in a particular location can influence soil characteristics. For example, soils in areas with high levels of rainfall tend to be more acidic, as rainwater can leach minerals from the soil and lower its pH. Similarly, soils in areas with high levels of sunlight and heat tend to be more alkaline, as the heat and sunlight can break down organic matter and increase the pH of the soil.

Vegetation, including plants and trees, can also influence soil formation, as they contribute organic matter and nutrients to the soil and help to protect it from erosion. Different plants and trees have different effects on soil, depending on their roots, the amount of leaf litter they produce, and the types of nutrients they contribute to the soil. For example, trees with deep root systems can help to anchor the soil and prevent erosion. In contrast, plants with shallow root systems may contribute more organic matter and nutrients to the soil.

Geology, including the type and composition of rock and minerals in an area, can also influence soil formation, as these materials can be broken down and weathered to form soil. In addition, the type and composition of rock and minerals in an area can influence the soil's characteristics, such as its texture, structure, and nutrient content.

The actions of living organisms, such as plants, animals, and microorganisms, can also influence soil formation, as they help to break down and decompose organic matter. **Microorganisms, such as bacteria and fungi, are important decomposers of organic matter and play a critical role in the nutrient-cycling process within the soil.** Animals, such as worms and insects, also contribute to the decomposition of organic matter and can help to improve soil structure and fertility.

Overall, many factors can influence soil formation. Therefore, understanding these factors is important for understanding how soil forms and changes over time and developing strategies for managing and conserving soil resources.

## Classification of Soils Based on Physical and Chemical Properties

Soil classification is the process of organizing and categorizing soils based on their physical and chemical properties. This is important for understanding different soils' characteristics and potential uses and developing appropriate management practices. Some common factors used in soil classification include texture, structure, pH, nutrient content, and organic matter content.

Soil texture refers to the size and proportions of the various particles that make up soil, including sand, silt, and clay. Soil structure refers to how these particles are arranged and held together and can be influenced by factors such as the presence of organic matter and the actions of living organisms. pH, or the acidity and alkalinity of the soil, is another important factor in soil classification, as different plants are better suited to different pH conditions. Nutrient content, including the levels of essential nutrients such as nitrogen, phosphorus, and potassium, is also an important factor in soil classification, as it can influence the health and productivity of plants. Finally, organic matter content, which refers to the amount of decomposed plant and animal material in soil, can also influence soil classification, as it helps to improve soil structure and fertility.

There are several different soil classification systems have been developed over the years, including the United States Department of Agriculture (USDA) soil taxonomy, the World Reference Base for Soil Resources (WRB), and the International Union of Soil Sciences (IUSS) soil classification system. These systems use different criteria and approaches to categorize soils. They may use different terms to describe the various soil types. However, all soil classification systems aim to provide a comprehensive and consistent way of organizing and categorizing soils based on their physical and chemical properties.

Understanding soil classification is important for understanding the characteristics and potential uses of different soils and for developing appropriate management practices that consider each soil type's unique properties and needs. This is especially important for agriculture, forestry, and other land use activities, as the health and productivity of the soil are directly related to the success of these activities. Soil classification is, therefore, a **vital tool for understanding and managing soil resources** and helps to ensure the long-term health and productivity of the soil.

Overall, soil classification is an important field of study within soil science and helps to understand better and manage soil resources. By understanding the physical, chemical, and biological properties of soils and how these properties interact, soil scientists can develop appropriate management practices that consider the unique characteristics and needs of different soil types. Soil classification is also important for identifying the potential uses of different soils and developing strategies for conserving and protecting soil resources. As soil is a critical natural resource essential for supporting plant growth and maintaining the health

of ecosystems, the ongoing study and understanding of soil classification are vital for ensuring our soil resources' long-term health
and productivity.

Ultimately, soil formation and classification are important
aspects of soil science, as they help us to understand the characteristics and potential uses of different soils. By studying the
processes of soil formation and the factors that influence it and
classifying soils based on their physical and chemical properties,
soil scientists can develop appropriate management practices and
advise on the sustainable use of soil resources. Understanding
these concepts is essential for ensuring our soil resources' long-
term health and productivity.

**Chapter Summary**

- Soil formation is the process of creating and developing soil over time. Various physical, chemical, and biological factors influence it.
- Physical factors influencing soil formation include climate, topography, and the actions of water, wind, and other weathering agents.
- Chemical factors that influence soil formation include the presence of minerals and organic matter and the effects of acidity and pH.
- Biological factors influencing soil formation include the actions of living organisms, such as plants, animals, and microorganisms.
- Climate, vegetation, geology, and the actions of living organisms are all factors that can influence soil formation.
- Soil classification is the process of organizing and categorizing soils based on their physical and chemical properties.
- Soil classification is important for understanding different soils' characteristics and potential uses and developing appropriate management practices.
- Soils can be classified based on various properties, including texture, structure, color, pH, and nutrient content.

**2**

———

# SOIL PHYSICAL PROPERTIES

T he physical properties of soil are important characteristics that influence its ability to support plant growth and other land use activities. Some of the key physical properties of soil include texture, structure, density, porosity, and water retention and drainage. In this chapter, we will explore these properties in more detail and discuss their significance in soil science.

## Texture and Structure of Soil

Soil texture is determined by the relative proportions of soil sand, silt, and clay particles. Sand particles are the largest and tend to be gritty and rough. Silt particles are smaller than sand and have a smooth, floury texture. Clay particles are the smallest and are very fine and smooth. We can determine the relative proportions of these particles in the soil through soil texture analysis, which involves using a set of standardized sieves to separate the particles by size.

The soil's texture can significantly impact its physical properties and ability to support plant growth. For example, soils with a high proportion of sand tend to be well-draining and have good aeration. Still, they may need better water retention and nutrient-holding capacity. Soils with a high proportion of clay tend to have good water retention and nutrient-holding capacity. Still, they may be poorly drained and prone to compaction. Soils with a high proportion of silt tend to have intermediate properties, with good water retention and drainage, but may be prone to erosion.

Soil structure refers to how the particles in soil are arranged and bonded together. Various factors influence soil structure, including the presence of **organic matter,** the actions of **living organisms,** and the influence of **water and other weathering agents.** Soils with a good structure tend to have well-defined pore spaces, which allow for good water and air movement and are more resistant to erosion and compaction. Conversely, soils with a poor structure tend to have poorly defined pore spaces, which can lead to problems with drainage and aeration and may be more prone to erosion and compaction.

Understanding the texture and structure of the soil is important for understanding its physical properties and potential uses. It can also help inform management practices, such as selecting appropriate crops and using appropriate tillage and irrigation techniques. Overall, the texture and structure of soil are important factors that influence its ability to support plant growth and maintain the health of ecosystems.

## Density and Porosity of Soil

The soil density is an important factor to consider when studying soil, as it can influence the soil's ability to support plant growth and the movement of water and nutrients through the soil. For example, soil that is too dense may have poor drainage and may be poorly aerated, which can limit the growth of plants. On the other hand, soil that is too porous may not be able to effectively retain water and nutrients, which can also negatively impact plant growth. Soil density and porosity can be affected by various factors, including the type and size of soil particles, the presence of organic matter, and the actions of living organisms.

Understanding soil density and porosity is important for managing soil resources, as it can help to optimize soil conditions for plant growth and to conserve water and nutrients. Techniques such as **tillage**, which involves mechanically breaking up the soil structure, can improve soil density and porosity. Soil amendments, such as adding organic matter or adjusting the pH, can also improve soil density and porosity. In addition, understanding soil density and porosity can be useful for predicting soil behavior under different conditions, such as during periods of drought or heavy rainfall.

Overall, soil density and porosity are important factors to consider when studying soil, as they can influence the soil's ability to support plant growth and retain water and nutrients. By understanding these properties and how we can manage them, soil scientists can help to optimize soil conditions for plant growth and to conserve important resources.

### Water Retention and Drainage in Soil

Various factors influence soil water retention and drainage, including soil texture, structure, density, and porosity. For example, soils with a high sand content tend to have poor water retention but good drainage. On the other hand, soils with a high clay content tend to have good water retention but poor drainage. **Soil structure** can also influence water retention and drainage, as soils with a well-developed structure tend to have better water retention and drainage than soils with a poorly developed structure. Finally, soil density and porosity can also influence these properties, as soils with a higher density and lower porosity tend to have poorer water retention and drainage compared to soils with a lower density and higher porosity.

In addition to these physical factors, chemical and biological factors can also influence soil water retention and drainage. For example, the presence of organic matter can help to improve water retention and drainage, as it helps to improve soil structure and increase the number of pores in the soil. In addition, the actions of living organisms, such as earthworms and microorganisms, can also influence water retention and drainage, as they help to break down organic matter and create pores in the soil.

Overall, water retention and drainage are important properties of soil that can significantly impact plant growth and ecosystem health. Therefore, understanding these properties and the factors that influence them is important for managing soil resources and optimizing plant growth.

Ultimately, the physical properties of soil are important characteristics that influence its ability to support plant growth and other land use activities. Understanding these properties and how they can be influenced by factors such as texture, structure, density, porosity, and water retention and drainage is essential for sustainably managing soil resources. By studying the physical properties of soil, soil scientists can develop techniques for conserving and improving soil quality and advise on the appropriate use of soil resources.

**Chapter Summary**

- The physical properties of soil include texture, structure, density, porosity, and water retention and drainage.
- Soil texture is determined by the relative proportions of soil sand, silt, and clay particles, which we can analyze through soil texture analysis.
- Soil structure refers to how the particles in soil are arranged and bonded together and is influenced by factors such as organic matter, living organisms, and weathering agents.
- Soil density and porosity can influence the soil's ability to support plant growth and the movement of water and nutrients through the soil.
- We can use techniques such as tillage and soil amendments to improve soil density and porosity.
- Soil water retention and drainage are important factors that influence plant growth and ecosystem health.
- Soil water retention is influenced by factors such as soil texture, structure, density, and porosity, as well as the presence of organic matter and soil pH.
- Understanding soil water retention and drainage is important for managing soil resources and predicting soil behavior under different conditions.

# 3

# SOIL CHEMICAL PROPERTIES

T he chemical properties of soil are important characteristics that influence its ability to support plant growth and other land use activities. Some of the key chemical properties of soil include pH, acidity, nutrient content, and soil organic matter. In this chapter, we will explore these properties in more detail and discuss their significance in soil science.

## pH and Acidity of Soil

Soil pH is an important factor in soil science, as it can significantly affect plants' health and productivity. Various factors, including the type and amount of minerals present, the presence of organic matter, and the actions of living organisms, can influence the pH of the soil. Some plants are more tolerant of acidic or basic soil conditions than others and may be more suited to certain pH ranges. For example, blueberries and rhododendrons grow best in acidic soil, while grasses and most vegetables prefer a more neutral pH.

Soil pH can be measured using various methods, including pH test strips, pH meters, and laboratory analyses. In addition, we can adjust soil pH by using lime or sulfur, which we can add to the soil to increase or decrease its pH. It is important to maintain an **appropriate pH range** for the plants being grown, as plants may be unable to absorb certain nutrients if the soil pH is too extreme.

Understanding soil pH and its effects on plant growth is an important aspect of soil science and helps to optimize soil fertility and plant productivity. It is also important to understand the ecological relationships between different plants and their soil environments and to develop sustainable land use practices.

## Nutrient Content of Soil

Soil nutrient content is an important factor in soil fertility and plant growth. Nutrients such as nitrogen, phosphorus, and potassium are essential for plant growth and development. They are typically classified as macronutrients because they are required in relatively large quantities. Other nutrients, such as micronutrients like zinc and iron, are also important but are needed in much smaller quantities. Soil nutrient content is influenced by various factors, including the type and composition of minerals in the soil, the presence of organic matter, and the soil's pH.

The availability of nutrients to plants is also influenced by soil pH, as certain nutrients are more readily available at certain pH levels. For example, nitrogen and phosphorus are typically more available to plants in soils with a pH between 6 and 7. At the same time, potassium is more readily available in soils with a pH between 5.5 and 7.5. In addition, soil organic matter, composed of decomposed plant and animal material, can also influence nutrient availability by serving as a source of nutrients and improving soil structure and water-holding capacity.

Soil testing is an important tool for assessing soil nutrient content and determining the fertilization needs of plants. Soil test results can help identify any nutrient deficiencies or excesses in the soil and inform the selection of appropriate fertilizers or other soil amendments to address these issues. Proper nutrient management is essential for optimizing plant growth and soil health. In addition, it can help to ensure that soil resources are used sustainably and efficiently.

## Soil Organic Matter and Its Role in Soil Fertility

Soil organic matter is formed through decomposition, in which microorganisms and other decomposers break down organic materials. This process releases nutrients that are then made available to plants and help improve the soil's structure and water-holding capacity. Soil organic matter is an important component of soil fertility, as it can help to improve the soil's ability to support plant growth and improve crop yields.

In addition to contributing essential nutrients, soil organic matter also plays a vital role in maintaining the health of the soil ecosystem. It supports the growth of beneficial microorganisms, such as bacteria and fungi, which are essential for breaking down organic matter and releasing nutrients. These microorganisms also help suppress the growth of harmful pathogens and pests, damaging plants and reducing crop yields.

The soil organic matter levels can vary widely depending on factors such as climate, vegetation, and land use practices. Soils rich in organic matter tend to be more fertile and productive and are better able to support plant growth. However, we can lose soil organic matter through various processes, including erosion, leaching, and the removal of organic materials through harvesting and other land use practices. Therefore, it is important to manage soil organic matter sustainably to maintain soil fertility and ecosystem health.

Overall, the chemical properties of soil are important characteristics that influence its ability to support plant growth and other land use activities. Understanding these properties and how they can be influenced by factors such as pH, acidity, nutrient content, and soil organic matter is essential for sustainably managing soil resources. By studying the chemical properties of soil, soil scientists can develop techniques for conserving and improving soil quality and advise on the appropriate use of soil resources.

**Chapter Summary**

- The chemical properties of soil include pH, acidity, nutrient content, and soil organic matter.
- Soil pH is an important factor influencing plant growth and productivity and can be measured and adjusted using various methods.
- Soil nutrient content is important for plant growth and development. It is influenced by factors such as the type and composition of minerals in the soil, the presence of organic matter, and the soil's pH.
- Soil testing is useful for assessing soil nutrient content and determining fertilization needs.
- Soil organic matter is formed through decomposition and is an important component of soil fertility. As a result, it can improve the soil's ability to support plant growth and crop yields.
- Soil organic matter also plays a vital role in maintaining the soil ecosystem's health and sequestering carbon from the atmosphere.
- Soil organic matter levels can be influenced by various factors, including the type and amount of organic materials added to the soil, the presence of living organisms, and the soil's pH and temperature.
- Understanding and managing soil organic matter are important for optimizing soil fertility and maintaining the soil ecosystem's health.

4
———

# SOIL BIOLOGICAL PROPERTIES

The biological properties of soil are important characteristics that influence its ability to support plant growth and other land use activities. Some of the key biological properties of soil include the presence of microorganisms and fauna and the role of soil biology in soil health and fertility. In this chapter, we will explore these properties in more detail and discuss their significance in soil science.

## Microorganisms in Soil

Microorganisms are essential to the **health and fertility of the soil**, as they help to break down and decompose organic matter, enriching the soil with essential nutrients. They also help to improve soil structure by producing substances that help to bind soil particles together. In addition, some microorganisms can fix nitrogen, converting atmospheric nitrogen into a form that plants use. This process is vital for the growth and productivity of plants, as nitrogen is an essential element required for synthesizing proteins and other important compounds.

Various factors, including soil pH, temperature, and moisture levels, influence the diversity of microorganisms in the soil. Soil management practices, such as using fertilizers, pesticides, and other chemicals, can also impact the populations of microorganisms in the soil. Understanding the role of microorganisms in soil is important for sustainably managing soil resources, as it can help to promote the growth and productivity of plants while also maintaining the health and fertility of the soil.

**Fauna in Soil**

The presence of microorganisms and fauna in the soil is crucial for maintaining soil health and fertility. These organisms play a vital role in decomposing organic matter and releasing nutrients into the soil, which is essential for plant growth and development. In addition, microorganisms and fauna help create and maintain soil structure, which can improve water retention and drainage and facilitate air and water movement through the soil. These organisms' activity can also help suppress plant diseases and pests, further improving crop yields.

Furthermore, a diverse and healthy community of microorganisms and fauna in the soil can improve soil structure and stability, leading to improved erosion control and reduced soil degradation. This is especially important in **agricultural and forestry settings**, where soil degradation can significantly negatively impact crop yields and ecosystem health. By understanding the role of soil biology in soil health and fertility and implementing management practices that support the growth and activity of these organisms, it is possible to improve the productivity and sustainability of soil resources.

## The Role of Soil Biology in Soil Health and Fertility

The health and fertility of the soil are largely determined by the balance and diversity of the biological community within it. When soil contains a diverse and healthy population of microorganisms and fauna, it is more resistant to degradation. As a result, it can support a wider range of plant species. On the other hand, when the biological community in the soil is imbalanced or depleted, it can lead to reduced fertility and increased susceptibility to erosion, compaction, and other forms of degradation.

Soil biology plays a vital role in nutrient cycling, which is essential for maintaining soil fertility. Microorganisms and soil fauna help break down organic matter and release nutrients, such as nitrogen, phosphorus, and potassium, which are essential for plant growth. They also help improve soil structure, which can enhance water retention and improve water infiltration and nutrients into the soil.

In addition to their role in nutrient cycling, soil microorganisms and fauna can also help suppress plant diseases and pests. For example, many soil-dwelling organisms produce antimicrobial compounds that can help control plant disease spread. In addition, some species of insects and worms feed on plant pests, helping to keep their populations in check.

Overall, the health and fertility of the soil are greatly influenced by the biological community within it. Therefore, understanding and managing soil's biological properties make it possible to enhance soil health and fertility and optimize the growth and productivity of crops and other plants.

Ultimately, the biological properties of soil are important characteristics that influence its ability to support plant growth and other land use activities. Understanding these properties and the role of soil biology in soil health and fertility is essential for sustainably managing soil resources. By studying the biological properties of soil, soil scientists can develop techniques for conserving and improving soil quality and advise on the appropriate use of soil resources.

## Chapter Summary

- The biological properties of soil include the presence of microorganisms and fauna and the role of soil biology in soil health and fertility.
- Microorganisms in soil are essential for breaking down and decomposing organic matter, enriching the soil with nutrients, and improving soil structure.
- The presence of fauna in the soil is important for decomposing organic matter, releasing nutrients, and maintaining soil structure.
- Soil biology is vital in maintaining soil health and fertility, including nutrient cycling, improving soil structure, and suppressing plant diseases and pests.
- The balance and diversity of the biological community in the soil are important for maintaining soil health and fertility, as an imbalanced or depleted population can lead to soil degradation.
- Soil management practices, such as using fertilizers and pesticides, can impact the populations of microorganisms and fauna in soil.
- Understanding the role of soil biology in soil health and fertility is important for sustainably managing soil resources and improving productivity.
- Techniques such as soil conservation, organic farming, and agroforestry can help promote the soil's health and fertility by supporting the growth and activity of the soil's biological community.

5
———

# SOIL FERTILITY AND NUTRIENT MANAGEMENT

S oil fertility refers to the ability of soil to support plant growth and other land-use activities. Various factors, including the availability of nutrients, the presence of organic matter, and the pH and acidity of the soil, influence soil fertility. Nutrient management is the process of ensuring that soils have an adequate supply of the nutrients that are necessary for plant growth. In this chapter, we will explore the role of nutrients in soil fertility and plant growth, the factors that influence nutrient availability in soil, and techniques for managing soil fertility, including fertilization and soil amendments.

## The Role of Nutrients in Soil Fertility and Plant Growth

Various factors, including soil pH, soil organic matter content, and the presence of certain minerals, influence the availability of nutrients in the soil. Acidic soils, for example, may have lower levels of available phosphorus. In comparison, alkaline soils may have lower levels of available iron. Soil organic matter content can also influence nutrient availability, as it helps release nutrients and act as a buffer to prevent nutrient loss. In addition, certain minerals in soil may interact with nutrients and influence their availability to plants.

Proper management of soil nutrients is essential for maintaining soil fertility and supporting healthy plant growth. This can include adding **fertilizers** to the soil to supplement nutrient levels and using techniques such as crop rotation and cover cropping to help maintain nutrient levels over time. It is also important to monitor soil nutrient levels and **address any imbalances**, as nutrient deficiencies or excesses can negatively impact plant growth and soil health.

Overall, understanding the role of nutrients in soil fertility and plant growth is important for proper soil management and maintaining healthy and productive soil resources. Understanding the factors that influence nutrient availability and implementing appropriate management practices makes it possible to maintain soil fertility and support healthy plant growth.

## Factors that Influence Nutrient Availability in Soil

The presence of certain minerals in the soil can also influence nutrient availability. For example, clay minerals can help hold onto certain nutrients, making them more available to plants. On the other hand, certain minerals, such as aluminum or manganese, can interfere with the availability of other nutrients, such as phosphorus.

The type and amount of vegetation in an area can also influence nutrient availability. For example, plant roots help extract nutrients from the soil, and the type of plants present can influence the types and amounts of nutrients taken up. In addition, the decomposition of plant material can release nutrients back into the soil, making them available to other plants.

Managing soil nutrients is important for maintaining soil fertility and supporting plant growth. This can involve adding nutrient-rich amendments, such as compost or fertilizers, to the soil and practicing sustainable land use practices that help preserve soil nutrients. Understanding the factors influencing nutrient availability in soil is essential for developing effective strategies for managing soil fertility.

## Techniques for Managing Soil Fertility

We can use several techniques to manage soil fertility and ensure that soils have an adequate supply of nutrients. These techniques include **fertilization** and the use of **soil amendments**. Fertilization is adding nutrients to the soil as fertilizers, synthetic or organic. Synthetic fertilizers are typically made from chemical compounds. They are designed to provide a specific set of nutrients to the soil. On the other hand, organic fertilizers are made from natural materials such as compost, animal manure, or green manure. They are typically more slowly released into the soil.

Soil amendments are added to soil to improve its physical and chemical properties, such as soil structure, water retention, and nutrient availability. Some common soil amendments include compost, lime, and gypsum. Compost is made from decomposed organic matter, such as plant debris and food waste. It can help to improve soil structure, water retention, and nutrient availability. Lime is a soil amendment made from ground limestone and used to adjust the pH of soil. Gypsum is a soil amendment made from calcium sulfate and is used to improve soil structure and drainage.

In addition to fertilization and the use of soil amendments, other techniques for managing soil fertility include crop rotation and the use of cover crops. Crop rotation is the practice of planting different crops yearly to help improve soil fertility and reduce the risk of soil-borne diseases. Cover crops are crops that are grown specifically to improve soil health rather than for harvest. In addition, cover crops can help to improve soil structure, suppress weeds, and reduce erosion.

Im summary, soil fertility and nutrient management are important aspects of soil science, as they are essential for maintaining the productivity and sustainability of soil resources. By understanding the role of nutrients in soil fertility and plant growth and studying the factors that influence nutrient availability in soil, soil scientists can develop techniques for managing soil fertility and optimizing crop yields. These techniques, including fertilization and soil amendments, can help ensure that soils have an adequate supply of the nutrients necessary for plant growth and development.

## Chapter Summary

- Soil fertility refers to the ability of soil to support plant growth and other land-use activities.
- Nutrient management ensures that soils have an adequate supply of the nutrients necessary for plant growth.
- Various factors, including soil pH, soil organic matter content, and certain minerals, influence the availability of nutrients in the soil.
- Proper management of soil nutrients is essential for maintaining soil fertility and supporting healthy plant growth.
- Techniques for managing soil fertility include fertilization and the use of soil amendments.
- Fertilization involves adding nutrients to the soil as fertilizers, synthetic or organic.
- Soil amendments are added to improve the physical and chemical properties of the soil, such as soil structure, water retention, and nutrient availability.
- Other techniques for managing soil fertility include crop rotation and cover crops.

6

---

# SOIL EROSION AND CONSERVATION

S oil erosion is the process by which soil is worn away or removed from an area, often due to the actions of water, wind, or other weathering agents. Soil erosion can significantly impact the productivity and sustainability of soil resources, leading to the loss of fertile soil, decreased water retention, and increased erosion of other natural resources. Soil conservation is protecting soil resources from erosion and other forms of degradation and maintaining or improving soil quality. In this chapter, we will explore the causes and impacts of soil erosion, techniques for preventing and controlling soil erosion, and the role of conservation practices in protecting soil resources.

## The Causes and Impacts of Soil Erosion

Soil erosion is the process by which soil is removed from its original location and transported elsewhere, often due to natural processes such as water, wind, and other weathering agents. However, human activities such as poor land management practices, deforestation, and overgrazing can also contribute to soil erosion.

33

Soil erosion can have serious consequences for the health and productivity of soil and the environment as a whole. It can lead to the loss of fertile soil, which is essential for supporting plant growth and maintaining the health of ecosystems. In addition, water or wind often carries away eroded soil, leading to the deterioration of other natural resources, such as water and air quality. Soil erosion can also contribute to biodiversity loss, as it can alter the habitats of plants and animals.

In addition to these environmental impacts, soil erosion can also have economic consequences, reducing land productivity and making it more difficult to grow crops. It can also increase the risk of natural disasters, such as landslides, which can cause damage to infrastructure and disrupt economic activity.

Overall, soil erosion is a serious problem that requires careful management and conservation efforts to mitigate its negative impacts. This may involve implementing measures such as terracing, contour plowing, and using cover crops to reduce erosion, as well as the restoration of degraded land.

## Techniques for Preventing and Controlling Soil Erosion

Preventing and controlling soil erosion is an important aspect of soil management, as it helps to protect and preserve valuable soil resources. One common technique for preventing soil erosion is using physical barriers, such as terracing and windbreaks. Terracing involves the construction of raised beds or ridges on slopes to help prevent soil erosion. In contrast, windbreaks involve planting trees or other vegetation to provide a physical barrier against the wind.

Another technique for preventing soil erosion is using vegetation to stabilize the soil. We can do this by using cover crops, which are planted specifically to protect soil from erosion and improve its overall health. Cover crops can also help to improve water retention and increase soil organic matter.

Mulches are another effective technique for preventing soil erosion. Mulches are materials, such as wood chips or straw, that are spread over the surface of the soil to protect it from erosion and improve water retention. Mulches can also help to regulate soil temperature and suppress weeds, making them an important tool for soil management.

Overall, physical barriers, vegetation, and mulches can effectively prevent and control soil erosion and are important tools for preserving valuable soil resources.

## The Role of Conservation Practices in Protecting Soil Resources

The adoption of conservation practices is becoming increasingly important as the global population continues to grow, and the demand for food, fuel, and other natural resources puts pressure on soil resources. Conservation practices help to preserve soil resources for future generations. They can also help mitigate climate change's impacts, as healthy soils are more resistant to drought and other extreme weather events. Some common conservation practices that we can use to protect soil resources include:

- **Crop rotation:** This involves planting different crops in a specific sequence, which can help to prevent soil erosion and depletion of nutrients.
- **Cover cropping:** This involves planting cover crops, such as legumes or grasses, between rows of main crops. Cover crops can help to protect soil from erosion, improve soil structure, and fix nitrogen in the soil.

- **Soil conservation tillage:** This involves using tillage techniques that minimize soil disturbance and reduce the impact of human activities on soil resources. These techniques can include no-till farming, strip tillage, and reduced tillage.
- **Erosion control:** Various techniques can be used to control erosion, such as physical barriers, vegetation, and cover crops. These techniques can help to reduce the impact of water, wind, and other weathering agents on soil resources.
- **Sustainable land management:** This involves adopting practices that balance the needs of humans with the health and sustainability of soil resources. This can include the use of organic farming techniques, the incorporation of conservation practices into land management plans, and the promotion of sustainable land use practices.

Overall, the adoption of conservation practices is an important step in protecting soil resources and ensuring the long-term sustainability of our natural resources.

Ultimately, soil erosion and conservation are important aspects of soil science, as they protect and preserve soil resources. By understanding the causes and impacts of soil erosion and studying techniques for preventing and controlling soil erosion, soil scientists can develop strategies for conserving and protecting soil resources. The use of conservation practices, such as sustainable land management practices, can also play a critical role in protecting soil resources and ensuring their long-term productivity and sustainability. By promoting the use of erosion control techniques and sustainable land management practices, soil scientists can help protect soil resources from erosion and other degradation forms and maintain or improve soil quality. These efforts are critical for ensuring the long-term productivity and sustainability of soil resources and supporting the growth of plants and other land use activities.

## Chapter Summary

- Soil erosion is the process by which soil is removed from its original location and transported elsewhere.
- Human activities, such as poor land management practices, deforestation, and overgrazing, can contribute to soil erosion.
- Soil erosion can lead to the loss of fertile soil and other natural resources, biodiversity loss, and economic consequences.
- Techniques for preventing soil erosion include physical barriers, terracing and windbreaks, vegetation, and mulches.
- Conservation practices, such as crop rotation, cover cropping, soil conservation tillage, erosion control, and sustainable land management, can help to protect soil resources.
- These efforts are critical for ensuring soil resources' long-term productivity and sustainability.
- Conservation practices can help to mitigate climate change's impacts, as healthy soils are more resistant to drought and other extreme weather events.
- By promoting erosion control techniques and sustainable land management practices, soil scientists can help protect soil resources from erosion and other degradation forms.

# 7

# SOIL MANAGEMENT IN AGRICULTURE

S oil management is an important aspect of agriculture, as it is essential for ensuring soil resources' long-term productivity and sustainability. Soil management practices can help to maintain or improve soil quality, optimize crop yields, and promote the growth of plants and other land use activities. In this chapter, we will explore the importance of soil management for sustainable agriculture, techniques for managing soil in different agricultural systems, and the role of soil science in optimizing crop yields and soil health.

## The Importance of Soil Management for Sustainable Agriculture

Effective soil management is essential for the long-term sustainability of agricultural systems. Soil is a vital resource that provides the foundation for plant growth and plays a key role in the health and productivity of agricultural systems. However, the soil is a finite resource and is vulnerable to degradation and erosion if not properly managed. Poor soil management practices, such as the overuse of chemical fertilizers and pesticides, can lead to soil degradation, which can decrease soil productivity and negatively impact the environment.

On the other hand, sustainable soil management practices can help maintain or improve soil quality, optimize crop yields, and promote the growth of plants and other land use activities in an environmentally sustainable way. These practices can include using cover crops, mulches, and other soil conservation techniques to reduce erosion and improve soil structure, as well as using organic fertilizers and other sustainable land management practices.

Effective soil management is also essential for addressing global challenges such as food security and climate change. Soil management practices that enhance soil fertility and promote sustainable agriculture can help to increase crop yields and improve food security in a changing climate. In addition, soil management practices that promote carbon sequestration and reduce greenhouse gas emissions can help to mitigate climate change and contribute to the long-term sustainability of agricultural systems. Overall, soil management is a critical component of sustainable agriculture and is essential for ensuring our agricultural systems' long-term health and productivity.

## Techniques for Managing Soil in Different Agricultural Systems

There are a variety of techniques that we can use to manage soil in different agricultural systems. These techniques can vary depending on the specific needs and characteristics of the soil and the type of crops being grown. Some common soil management practices in agriculture include using cover crops, mulches, and fertilizers, as well as implementing sustainable land management practices such as conservation tillage and integrated pest management. These practices can help to improve soil structure, fertility, and productivity, as well as reduce the impact of agriculture on the environment.

One technique that is commonly used to manage soil in agriculture is the use of **cover crops.** Cover crops are grown specifically to protect soil and improve its physical and chemical properties. For example, cover crops can help to prevent erosion, reduce the need for chemical fertilizers, and improve soil structure and water retention. They can also help suppress weeds and pests and provide a habitat for beneficial insects and other wildlife.

Mulches are another important tool for soil management in agriculture. Mulches are materials, such as straw or wood chips, applied to the soil surface to help protect it from erosion, retain moisture, and suppress weeds. Mulches can be used in various agricultural systems, including row crops, orchards, and gardens.

Fertilizers are another common soil management practice in agriculture. Fertilizers are materials applied to soil to give plants the nutrients they need to grow and develop. Many different types of fertilizers are available, including synthetic fertilizers and organic fertilizers. Synthetic fertilizers are made from inorganic chemicals, while organic fertilizers are made from natural materials such as compost or animal manure.

Sustainable land management practices, such as conservation tillage and integrated pest management, are also important tools for managing soil in agriculture. Conservation tillage is a technique that involves minimizing soil disturbance during planting and harvesting, which can help to reduce erosion and improve soil structure. Integrated pest management is a technique that involves using a variety of strategies, such as biological control and cultural practices, to manage pests in a way that is sustainable and environmentally friendly.

We can use many techniques to manage soil in different agricultural systems. The most appropriate techniques will depend on the specific needs and characteristics of the soil and the crops being grown. Using a combination of cover crops, mulches, fertilizers, and sustainable land management practices, we can optimize soil productivity and reduce the impact of agriculture on the environment.

## The Role of Soil Science in Optimizing Crop Yields and Soil Health

Soil science is critical in optimizing crop yields and soil health in agricultural systems. By studying soil's physical, chemical, and biological properties, soil scientists can develop techniques for managing soil in a way that maximizes crop yields and promotes soil health. This can involve using fertilizers, soil amendments, and other techniques to optimize nutrient availability, improve soil structure, and promote the growth of beneficial microorganisms.

Im summary, soil management is an essential aspect of agriculture, as it is critical for ensuring the long-term productivity and sustainability of soil resources. By understanding the importance of soil management for sustainable agriculture and studying techniques for managing soil in different agricultural systems, soil scientists can develop strategies for optimizing crop yields and promoting soil health. The role of soil science in this process is critical, as it provides the knowledge and tools needed to understand and manage soil resources in a productive and sustainable way. Furthermore, by applying this knowledge, soil scientists can help to ensure that agricultural systems can support the growth of plants and other land use activities in a sustainable and environmentally responsible way.

## Chapter Summary

- Soil management is essential for the long-term sustainability of agricultural systems.
- Poor soil management practices can lead to soil degradation, negatively affecting the environment.
- Sustainable soil management practices can help to maintain or improve soil quality and optimize crop yields.
- Effective soil management is also essential for addressing global challenges such as food security and climate change.
- Techniques for managing soil in different agricultural systems include using cover crops, mulches, and fertilizers and implementing sustainable land management practices.
- Soil science is critical in optimizing crop yields and soil health in agricultural systems.
- By studying soil's physical, chemical, and biological properties, soil scientists can develop techniques for managing soil to maximize crop yields and promote soil health.
- Soil science provides the knowledge and tools to understand and manage soil resources productively and sustainably.

# 8

## SOIL MANAGEMENT IN FORESTRY AND LANDSCAPING

S oil management is an important aspect of forestry and landscaping, as it is essential for ensuring the long-term productivity and sustainability of soil resources in these settings. In addition, soil management practices can help to maintain or improve soil quality, optimize the growth of trees and other plants, and promote the health and beauty of landscapes. In this chapter, we will explore the role of soil science in managing forest and landscape soils, techniques for conserving and improving soil quality in these settings, and the impact of land use practices on soil resources.

## The Role of Soil Science in Managing Forest and Landscape Soils

Soil science plays a critical role in managing forest and landscape soils, as it provides the knowledge and tools needed to understand and manage soil resources in these settings. By studying soil's physical, chemical, and biological properties, soil scientists can develop techniques for managing soil to maximize the growth of trees and other plants and promote soil health. This can involve the use of fertilizers, soil amendments, and other techniques to optimize nutrient availability, improve soil structure, and promote the growth of beneficial microorganisms.

## Techniques for Conserving and Improving Soil Quality in these Settings

There are a variety of techniques that we can use to conserve and improve soil quality in forestry and landscaping settings. These techniques can vary depending on the specific needs and characteristics of the soil and the type of plants being grown. Some common soil management practices in these settings include using cover crops, mulches, and fertilizers, as well as implementing sustainable land management practices such as conservation tillage and integrated pest management.

*To learn more about these soils management practices, revisit chapter 7.*

## The Impact of Land Use Practices on Soil Resources

How land is used can have a significant impact on soil resources. For example, poor land use practices, such as deforestation and overgrazing, can lead to soil degradation, decreasing soil productivity and negatively impacting the environment. By contrast, sustainable land use practices, such as sustainable forestry and landscaping, can help maintain or improve soil quality, optimize the growth of trees and other plants, and promote the health and beauty of landscapes in a sustainable way.

In summary, soil management is an essential aspect of forestry and landscaping, as it is critical for ensuring the long-term productivity and sustainability of soil resources in these settings. By understanding the role of soil science in managing forest and landscape soils and studying techniques for conserving and improving soil quality in these settings, soil scientists can develop strategies for optimizing the growth of trees and other plants and promoting soil health. The impact of land use practices on soil resources is also an important consideration, as how land is used can have significant consequences for soil quality and productivity. By applying this knowledge, soil scientists can help ensure that forestry and landscaping practices can support the growth of trees and other plants in a sustainable and environmentally responsible way.

## Chapter Summary

- Soil science plays a critical role in managing forest and landscape soils.
- There are a variety of techniques that we can use to conserve and improve soil quality in forestry and landscaping settings.
- Poor land use practices can lead to soil degradation, while sustainable land use practices can help maintain or improve soil quality.
- Soil management is essential for ensuring the long-term productivity and sustainability of soil resources in these settings.
- By understanding the role of soil science and studying techniques for conserving and improving soil quality, soil scientists can develop strategies for optimizing the growth of trees and other plants and promoting soil health.
- The impact of land use practices on soil resources is also an important consideration.
- By applying this knowledge, soil scientists can help ensure that forestry and landscaping practices can support the growth of trees and other plants in a sustainable and environmentally responsible way.

# 9

# SOIL MANAGEMENT IN ENVIRONMENTAL RESTORATION

E nvironmental restoration is rehabilitating degraded or damaged ecosystems to return them to a more natural and functional state. Soil management is an important aspect of environmental restoration. The soil is a vital component of ecosystems. It is critical for supporting the growth of plants and other land-use activities. In this chapter, we will explore the role of soil science in environmental restoration projects, techniques for rehabilitating degraded soils, and the importance of soil health in maintaining ecosystem function.

### The Role of Soil Science in Environmental Restoration Projects

Soil science is a key discipline in environmental restoration, as it helps to understand and manage soil resources to promote the growth of plants and restore ecosystem function. Soil scientists use various techniques to improve soil quality, including using fertilizers, soil amendments, and sustainable land management practices such as conservation tillage and integrated pest management.

These techniques are designed to **optimize nutrient availability**, **improve soil structure**, and **promote the growth of bene-**

**ficial microorganisms**, all of which are critical for the success of environmental restoration projects. In addition, soil scientists also work to understand the impacts of environmental stressors, such as pollution and climate change, on soil health to develop strategies for mitigating these impacts and promoting soil recovery. Overall, the role of soil science in environmental restoration is crucial in ensuring the long-term sustainability of our natural resources.

## Techniques for Rehabilitating Degraded Soils

To effectively rehabilitate degraded soils, assessing the underlying causes of soil degradation is important. This can involve studying the soil's physical, chemical, and biological properties, as well as evaluating the potential impact of human activities such as deforestation and overgrazing. Once the causes of soil degradation have been identified, appropriate techniques can be selected and implemented to restore soil quality and promote the growth of plants and other land-use activities.

One important aspect of soil rehabilitation is the use of cover crops and mulches. These techniques involve planting crops or applying organic materials to the soil surface, which can help improve soil structure, reduce erosion, and promote the growth of beneficial microorganisms. Cover crops and mulches can also help to improve soil water retention, which is important for supporting plant growth in areas with limited water resources.

In addition, to cover crops and mulches, fertilizers and other soil amendments can be used to improve soil nutrient availability and promote plant growth. However, it is important to use these techniques judiciously, as **over-fertilization** can lead to soil degradation and negative environmental impacts. Instead, it is often more effective to implement sustainable land management practices that take into account the long-term health and productivity of the soil. This can include techniques such as conservation tillage, which involves minimizing the disturbance of soil and preserving soil structure, and integrated pest management, which involves using natural methods for controlling pests and diseases.

## The Importance of Soil Health in Maintaining Ecosystem Function

Soil health is critical for maintaining ecosystem function, as it is essential for supporting the growth of plants and other land-use activities. Degraded soils can *negatively* impact ecosystem function, as they may be less able to support the growth of plants and other land use activities. By rehabilitating degraded soils and promoting soil health, it is possible to sustainably restore ecosystem function and support the growth of plants and other land use activities.

In summary, soil management is an important aspect of environmental restoration, as it is critical for ensuring the long-term productivity and sustainability of soil resources in these settings. By understanding the role of soil science in environmental restoration projects and studying techniques for rehabilitating degraded soils, soil scientists can develop strategies for restoring ecosystem function and promoting the growth of plants and other land use activities. The importance of soil health in maintaining ecosystem function is also an important consideration, as soil health is essential for sustainably supporting the growth of plants and other land-use activities. By applying this knowledge, soil scientists can help to ensure that environmental restoration efforts can restore ecosystems practically and sustainably.

## Chapter Summary

- Environmental restoration is rehabilitating degraded or damaged ecosystems to return them to a more natural and functional state.
- Soil science is a key discipline in environmental restoration, as it helps to understand and manage soil resources to promote the growth of plants and restore ecosystem function.
- Techniques for rehabilitating degraded soils include using fertilizers, soil amendments, and sustainable land management practices such as conservation tillage and integrated pest management.
- Cover crops and mulches are important techniques for improving soil structure, reducing erosion, and promoting the growth of beneficial microorganisms.
- Fertilizers and other soil amendments can improve nutrient availability and promote plant growth.
- Soil health is critical for maintaining ecosystem function, as it is essential for supporting the growth of plants and other land-use activities.
- By understanding the role of soil science in environmental restoration projects and studying techniques for rehabilitating degraded soils, soil scientists can develop strategies for restoring ecosystem function and promoting the growth of plants and other land-use activities.
- The importance of soil health in maintaining ecosystem function is essential for sustainably supporting the growth of plants and other land-use activities.

# 10

## SOIL MANAGEMENT IN URBAN AND
## INDUSTRIAL SETTINGS

S oil management is an important aspect of urban and industrial areas, as it is essential for ensuring the long-term productivity and sustainability of soil resources in these settings. In addition, soil management practices can help to maintain or improve soil quality, optimize the growth of plants and other land use activities, and promote the health and beauty of urban and industrial environments. In this chapter, we will explore the challenges of managing soil in urban and industrial areas, techniques for conserving and improving soil quality in these settings, and the role of soil science in designing and managing green spaces in urban areas.

### The Challenges of Managing Soil in Urban and Industrial Areas

Managing soil in urban and industrial areas can be challenging, as these environments often have unique soil conditions and characteristics that can be difficult to manage. In addition, urban and industrial soils may be subjected to various stressors, such as pollution, compaction, and alteration, which can negatively impact soil quality and productivity. For example, we may contaminate urban and industrial soils with heavy metals or other toxic substances, which can make them inhospitable to plants and other living organisms.

Additionally, the lack of space and other constraints in urban and industrial areas can make it difficult to implement traditional soil management practices, such as using cover crops and mulches or applying fertilizers and other soil amendments. These challenges highlight the importance of developing innovative approaches to soil management in urban and industrial areas to ensure that these soils can support the growth of plants and other land-use activities in a sustainable way.

## Techniques for Conserving and Improving Soil Quality in these Settings

Managing soil in urban and industrial areas can be challenging due to the unique conditions and characteristics that these environments often present. Urban and industrial soils may be subjected to various stressors such as pollution, compaction, and alteration, which can affect soil quality and productivity negatively. In addition, urban and industrial areas' space constraints and other factors can make it difficult to implement traditional soil management practices.

Therefore, it is important to use techniques specifically tailored to these environments' needs to conserve and improve soil quality. Some common techniques include using cover crops, mulches, and fertilizers, as well as implementing sustainable land management practices such as conservation tillage and integrated pest management. These techniques can help to maintain or improve soil quality, optimize plant growth, and promote sustainable land use in urban and industrial areas.

*To learn more about these soils management practices, revisit chapter 7.*

## The Role of Soil Science in Designing and Managing Green Spaces in Urban Areas

Soil science plays a critical role in designing and managing green spaces in urban areas, as it provides the knowledge and tools needed to understand and manage soil resources in these settings. By studying the physical, chemical, and biological properties of soil, soil scientists are able to develop techniques for managing soil in a way that promotes the growth of plants and other land-use activities and enhances the health and beauty of urban environments. This can involve using fertilizers, soil amendments, and other techniques to optimize nutrient availability, improve soil structure, and promote the growth of beneficial microorganisms.

In summary, soil management is an important aspect of urban and industrial areas, as it is critical for ensuring the long-term productivity and sustainability of soil resources in these settings. By understanding the challenges of managing soil in urban and industrial areas and by studying techniques for conserving and improving soil quality in these settings, soil scientists can develop strategies for optimizing the growth of plants and other land-use activities and promoting the health and beauty of urban environments. The role of soil science in designing and managing green spaces in urban areas is also important, as soil science provides the knowledge and tools needed to understand and manage soil resources in these settings practically and sustainably.

## Chapter Summary

- Soil management is an important aspect of urban and industrial areas.
- Managing soil in urban and industrial areas can be challenging due to the unique conditions and characteristics of these environments.
- Techniques such as using cover crops, mulches, and fertilizers, as well as implementing sustainable land management practices, can help to conserve and improve soil quality.
- Soil science plays a critical role in designing and managing green spaces in urban areas, as it provides the knowledge and tools needed to sustainably understand and manage soil resources.

# EPILOGUE

S oil science is a critical field that is essential for understanding and managing soil resources. Soil is a vital component of ecosystems and is critical for supporting the growth of plants and other land-use activities. In this final chapter, we will explore the importance of soil science in understanding and managing soil resources, and the ongoing need for research and innovation in the field.

## The Importance of Soil Science in Understanding and Managing Soil Resources

Soil science plays a critical role in understanding and managing soil resources, as it provides the knowledge and tools needed to understand and manage soil in a productive and sustainable way. By studying soil's physical, chemical, and biological properties, soil scientists can develop techniques for managing soil in a way that promotes the growth of plants and other land use activities and maintains or improves soil quality. This knowledge is essential for a variety of applications, including agriculture, forestry and landscaping, environmental restoration, and urban and industrial settings.

## The Ongoing Need for Research and Innovation in the Field

Despite the importance of soil science, much still needs to be discovered about soil and its role in ecosystems. As a result, there is a continuing need for research and innovation in the field of soil science. By studying the properties of soil and developing new techniques for managing soil resources, soil scientists can improve our understanding of soil and its role in supporting the growth of plants and other land-use activities. This knowledge is critical for developing strategies for optimizing soil productivity and sustainability and addressing the future challenges that soil resources face.

In summary, soil science is a required field that is essential for understanding and managing soil resources. By studying soil's physical, chemical, and biological properties, soil scientists can develop techniques for managing soil in a way that promotes the growth of plants and other land use activities and maintains or improves soil quality. The ongoing need for research and innovation in soil science is also important, as it allows us to continue to improve our understanding of soil and its role in ecosystems and to develop new strategies for optimizing soil productivity and sustainability. By applying this knowledge, soil scientists can make important contributions to a wide range of fields and help ensure that soil resources can support the growth of plants and other land-use activities in a sustainable way.

# ACKNOWLEDGMENTS

I want to express my sincere gratitude to all of the individuals who have supported me throughout the writing of this book.

First and foremost, I thank my family for their unwavering support and encouragement. Their love and belief in me have kept me going during the many long nights spent researching and writing.

I also want to thank my colleagues and mentors in soil science, who have generously shared their knowledge and expertise with me. Their guidance and support have been invaluable in helping me to understand and present the complex concepts contained in this book.

Finally, I thank my editor and publisher for their patience and hard work in bringing this book to fruition. Their dedication to producing a high-quality product is greatly appreciated.

To all of these people and more, thank you for helping to make this book a reality.

# ABOUT THE AUTHOR

Michael Barton is an expert in sustainability and regenerative agriculture with over a decade of experience. He holds a degree in Environmental Studies and has received advanced training in the principles and practices of regenerative agriculture.

Throughout his career, Michael has worked with farmers, policymakers, and environmentalists to promote sustainable farming practices and advocate for the adoption of regenerative agriculture. He has collaborated with organizations worldwide to advance sustainable agriculture and food systems.

In his book, *Introduction to Soil Science*, Michael shares his expertise and experience to provide a comprehensive guide to the fundamental principles of soil science. The book covers a wide range of topics, including soil formation and classification, physical, chemical, and biological properties of soil, fertility and nutrient management, erosion and conservation, and soil management.

With a focus on practical applications, the book equips readers with the knowledge and skills to effectively understand and manage soil resources. Michael's passion for sustainability and his belief in the importance of soil health shines through on every page of this valuable resource.

Receive Your Free Copy of Self-Sufficient Homesteading

Or visit:
bookboundstudios.wixsite.com/michael-barton

Printed in Great Britain
by Amazon